VICTORIA'S
∽ WORDS OF ∽
LOVE

VICTORIA'S
∽ WORDS OF ∽
LOVE

VOLUME ONE

VICTORIA'S SECRET

Nº 10 MARGARET STREET
LONDON W1

FOR AS LONG as men and
women have written of their
inmost feelings, love has been
their inspiration. Serenading
or pleading, wooing, rhap-
sodizing or languishing, they
have immortalized their loves
in some of the most beautiful
and moving words ever written. I have chosen the poetry
and prose in this treasury from this great wealth of literature to
reflect love in all its moods – passionate or lyrical, urgent or
pensive, rapturous or melancholy.

Some pieces, perhaps the most familiar, will probably
always remain unsurpassed as expressions of love: nothing can
equal the exquisitely tender reverence of Shakespeare's 'Shall I
compare thee to a summer's day?', for example, or the
devastating candour of Elizabeth Barrett Browning's 'If thou

must love me, let it be for nought except for love's sake only'. Others have been included for their poignant innocence, their melting sensuality, their wry humour, their lyrical tenderness or their burning passion. All of them express – sometimes with infinite delicacy, sometimes with startling power – the feelings which every lover knows, from the delicious uncertainties of first love to the ecstasies of love fulfilled.

I have matched each passage of love to a painting which perfectly expresses the infinitely subtle moods within each story and which is also astoundingly beautiful in its own right. My choice has inevitably included paintings by those unashamedly romantic Victorian artists, for there can be nothing more lovely than their description of wistful women in flowing robes, detailed with satin sashes and lace, or more dashing than their portrayal of the young gentleman of Victorian England. They perfectly complement these words of love, and reiterate the conviction deep in every lover's heart which Keats expressed when he declared 'No one has ever loved but you and I'.

With Love

THE NYMPH'S REPLY

If all the world and love were young,
And truth in every shepherd's tongue,
These pretty pleasures might me move
To live with thee and be thy Love.

But Time drives flocks from field to fold;
When rivers rage and rocks grow cold;
And Philomel becometh dumb;
The rest complains of cares to come.

The flowers do fade, and wanton fields
To wayward Winter reckoning yields:
A honey tongue, a heart of gall,
Is fancy's spring, but sorrow's fall.

But could youth last, and love still breed,
Had joys no date, nor age no need,
Then these delights my mind might move
To live with thee and be thy Love.

SIR WALTER RALEGH 1552–1618

[7]

THE FIRST DAY

I wish I could remember the first day,
First hour, first moment of your meeting me;
If bright or dim the season, it might be
Summer or winter for aught I can say.
So unrecorded did it slip away,
So blind was I to see and to foresee,
So dull to mark the budding of my tree
That would not blossom yet for many a May.
If only I could recollect it! Such
A day of days! I let it come and go
As traceless as a thaw of bygone snow.
It seemed to mean so little, meant so much!
If only now I could recall that touch,
First touch of hand in hand! – Did one but know!

CHRISTINA ROSSETTI 1834–94

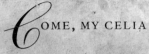

COME, MY CELIA

Come, my Celia, let us prove,
While we can, the sports of love.
Time will not be ours for ever;
He, at length, our good will sever.
Spend not then his gifts in vain:
Suns that set may rise again.
But if once we lose this light,
'Tis with us perpetual night.
Why should we defer our joys?
Fame and rumour are but toys.
Cannot we delude the eyes
Of a few poor household spies?
Or his easier ears beguile,
Thus removéd by our wile?
'Tis no sin love's fruits to steal,
But the sweet thefts to reveal;
To be taken, to be seen,
These have crimes accounted been.

BEN JONSON 1573–1637

DREAMS OF THEE

I arise from dreams of thee
In the first sweet sleep of night,
When the winds are breathing low,
And the stars are shining bright:
I arise from dreams of thee,
And a spirit in my feet
Hath led me – who knows how?
To thy chamber window, Sweet!

Oh lift me from the grass!
I die! I faint! I fail!
Let thy love in kisses rain
On my lips and eyelids pale.
My cheek is cold and white, alas!
My heart beats loud and fast; –
Oh! press it to thine own again,
Where it will break at last.

PERCY BYSSHE SHELLEY 1792–1822

STILL TO BE NEAT

Still to be neat, still to be drest,
As you were going to a feast;
Still to be powdered, still perfumed:
Lady, it is to be presumed.
Though art's hid causes are not found,
All is not sweet, all is not sound.

Give me a look, give me a face,
That makes simplicity a grace;
Robes loosely flowing, hair as free:
Such sweet neglect more taketh me,
Than all th' adulteries of art.
They strike mine eyes, but not my hear .

BEN JONSON 1573–1637

ℒORD ORVILLE DECLARES HIMSELF

We all went together to the drawing-room. After a short and unentertaining conversation, Mrs Selwyn said she must prepare for her journey, and begged me to see for some books she had left in the parlour.

And here, while I was looking for them, I was followed by Lord Orville. He shut the door after he came in, and approaching me with a look of anxiety, said, 'Is this true, Miss Anville? are you going?'

'I believe so, my Lord,' said I, still looking for the books.

'So suddenly, so unexpectedly, must I lose you?'

'No great loss, my Lord,' cried I, endeavouring to speak chearfully.

'Is it possible', said he, gravely, 'Miss Anville can doubt my sincerity?'

'I can't imagine,' cried I, 'what Mrs Selwyn has done with these books.'

'Would to Heaven,' continued he, 'I might flatter myself you would allow me to prove it!'

'I must run up stairs,' cried I, greatly confused, 'and ask what she has done with them.'

'You are going, then,' cried he, taking my hand, 'and you give me not the smallest hope of your return! – will you not, then, my too lovely friend! – will you not, at least, teach me, with fortitude like your own, to support your absence?'

'My Lord,' cried I, endeavouring to disengage my hand, 'pray let me go!'

'I will,' cried he, to my inexpressible confusion, dropping on one knee, 'if you wish to leave me!'

'Oh, my Lord,' exclaimed I, 'rise, I beseech you, rise! – such a posture to me! – surely your Lordship is not so cruel as to mock me!'

'Mock you!' repeated he earnestly; 'no, I revere you! I esteem and I admire you above all human beings! you are the friend to whom my soul is attached as to its better half! you are the most amiable, the most perfect of women! and you are dearer to me than language has the power of telling.'

I cannot write the scene that followed, though every word is engraven on my heart: but his protestations, his expressions, were too flattering for repetition: nor would he, in spite of my repeated efforts to leave him, suffer me to escape; – in short, my dear Sir, I was not proof against his solicitations – and he drew from me the most sacred secret of my heart!

Evelina, FANNY BURNEY 1752–1840

[17]

Upon Julia's Clothes

When as in silks my Julia goes,
Then, then (me thinks) how sweetly flows
The liquefaction of her clothes.

Next, when I cast mine eyes and see
That brave vibration each way free,
O how that glittering taketh me!

ROBERT HERRICK 1591–1674

$\mathcal{M}$OTHER, I CANNOT MIND MY WHEEL

Mother, I cannot mind my wheel;
   My fingers ache, my lips are dry:
Oh! if you felt the pain I feel!
   But Oh, who ever felt as I?

No longer could I doubt him true;
   All other men may use deceit:
He always said my eyes were blue,
   And often swore my lips were sweet.

WALTER SAVAGE LANDOR 1775–1864

Song

Hears not my Phillis how the birds
   Their feathered mates salute!
They tell their Passion in their words;
   Must I alone be mute?
     Phillis, without frown or smile,
     Sat and knotted all the while!

The God of Love, in thy bright eyes,
   Does like a tyrant reign!
But in thy heart, a child he lies,
   Without his dart, or flame!
     Phillis, without frown or smile,
     Sat and knotted all the while!

So many months, in silence past,
   (And yet in raging love)
Might well deserve One Word, at last.
   My Passion should approve!
     Phillis, without frown or smile,
     Sat and knotted all the while!

Must then, your faithful Swain expire?
   And not one look obtain?
Which he, to sooth his fond Desire,
   Might pleasingly explain!
     Phillis, without frown or smile,
     Sat and knotted all the while!

SIR CHARLES SEDLEY 1639–1701

Now is my love all ready forth to come:
Let all the virgins therefore well await;
And ye, fresh boys, that tend upon her groom,
Prepare yourselves, for he is coming straight.

Epithalamion, EDMUND SPENSER 1552–99

I DO NOT *L*OVE THEE

I do not love thee! – no! I do not love thee!
And yet when thou art absent I am sad;
   And envy even the bright blue sky above thee,
Whose quiet stars may see thee and be glad.

I do not love thee! – yet, I know not why,
Whate'er thou dost seems still well done, to me:
   And often in my solitude I sigh
That those I do love are not more like thee!

I do not love thee! – yet, when thou art gone,
I hate the sound (though those who speak be dear)
   Which breaks the lingering echo of the tone
Thy voice of music leaves upon my ear.

I do not love thee! – yet thy speaking eyes,
With their deep, bright, and most expressive blue,
   Between me and the midnight heaven arise,
Oftener than any eyes I ever knew.

I know I do not love thee! yet, alas!
Others will scarcely trust my candid heart;
   And oft I catch them smiling as they pass,
Because they see me gazing where thou art.

CAROLINE NORTON 1808–77

[25]

 HALL I COMPARE THEE
TO A SUMMER'S DAY

Shall I compare thee to a summer's day?
Thou art more lovely and more temperate:
Rough winds do shake the darling buds of May,
And summer's lease hath all too short a date:
Sometime too hot the eye of heaven shines,
And often is his gold complexion dimmed;
And every fair from fair sometime declines,
By chance, or nature's changing course untrimmed:
But thy eternal summer shall not fade,
Nor lose possession of that fair thou ow'st,
Nor shall death brag thou wander'st in his shade,
When in eternal lines to time thou grow'st;
   So long as men can breathe, or eyes can see,
   So long lives this, and this gives life to thee.

WILLIAM SHAKESPEARE 1564–1616

LOVE AND MR LEWISHAM

For three indelible days Lewisham's existence was a fabric of fine emotions, life was too wonderful and beautiful for any doubts or forethought. To be with Ethel was perpetual delight – she astonished this sisterless youngster with a thousand feminine niceties and refinements. She shamed him for his strength and clumsiness. And the light in her eyes and the warmth in her heart that lit them!

On Sunday evening they went for a long rambling walk through the quiet streets, coming out at last into Hyde Park. The early spring night was mild and clear and the kindly moonlight was about them. They went to the bridge and looked down the Serpentine, with the little lights of Paddington yellow and remote. They stood there, dim little figures and very close together. They whispered and became silent.

Presently it seemed that something passed and Lewisham began talking in his magnificent vein. He likened the Serpentine to Life, and found Meaning in the dark banks of Kensington Gardens and the remote bright lights. 'The long struggle,' he said, 'and the lights at the end,' – though he really did not know what he meant by the lights at the end. Neither did Ethel, though the emotion was indisputable. 'We are Fighting the World,' he said, finding great satisfaction in the thought. 'All the world is against us – and we are fighting it all.'

'We will not be beaten,' said Ethel.

'How could we be beaten – together?' said Lewisham. 'For you I would fight a dozen worlds.'

It seemed a very sweet and noble thing to them under the sympathetic moonlight, almost indeed too easy for their courage, to be merely fighting the world.

Love and Mr Lewisham, H. G. WELLS 1866–1946

[29]

SWEET DISORDER

A sweet disorder in the dress
Kindles in clothes a wantonness:
A lawn about the shoulders thrown
Into a fine distraction –
An erring lace, which here and there
Enthrals the crimson stomacher –
A cuff neglectful, and thereby
Ribbands to flow confusedly –
A winning wave, deserving note,
In the tempestuous petticoat –
A careless shoe-string, in whose tie
I see a wild civility –
Do more bewitch me than when art
Is too precise in every part.

ROBERT HERRICK 1591–1674

CATHERINE'S SECRET

'What are you thinking of so earnestly?' said he, as they walked back to the ball-room; – 'not of your partner, I hope, for, by that shake of the head, your meditations are not satisfactory.'

Catherine coloured, and said, 'I was not thinking of any thing.'

'That is artful and deep, to be sure; but I had rather be told at once that you will not tell me.'

'Well then, I will not.'

'Thank you; for now we shall soon be acquainted, as I am authorized to tease you on this subject whenever we meet, and nothing in the world advances intimacy so much.'

They danced again; and, when the assembly closed, parted, on the lady's side at least, with a strong inclination for continuing the acquaintance. Whether she thought of him so much, while she drank her warm wine and water, and prepared herself for bed, as to dream of him when there, cannot be ascertained; but I hope it was no more than in a slight slumber, or a morning doze at most; for if it be true, as a celebrated writer has maintained, that no young lady can be justified in falling in love before the gentleman's love is declared, it must be very improper that a young lady should dream of a gentleman before the gentleman is first known to have dreamt of her.

Northanger Abbey, JANE AUSTEN 1775–1817

TO THE VIRGINS,
TO MAKE MUCH OF TIME

Gather ye Rose-buds while ye may,
  Old Time is still a flying:
And this same flower that smiles to day,
  To morrow will be dying.

The glorious Lamp of Heaven, the Sun,
  The higher he's a getting;
The sooner will his Race be run,
  And neerer he's to Setting.

That Age is best, which is the first,
  When Youth and Blood are warmer;
But being spent, the worse, and worst
  Times, still succeed the former.

Then be not coy, but use your time;
  And while ye may, goe marry:
For having lost but once your prime,
  You may for ever tarry.

ROBERT HERRICK 1591–1674

If THOU MUST LOVE ME

If thou must love me, let it be for nought
Except for love's sake only. Do not say
'I love her for her smile . . her look . . her way
Of speaking gently, . . for a trick of thought
That falls in well with mine, and certes brought
A sense of pleasant ease on such a day' –
For these things in themselves, Beloved, may
Be changed, or change for thee, – and love so wrought,
May be unwrought so. Neither love me for
Thine own dear pity's wiping my cheeks dry,
Since one might well forget to weep who bore
Thy comfort long, and lose thy love thereby,
But love me for love's sake, that evermore
Thou may'st love on through love's eternity.

ELIZABETH BARRETT BROWNING 1806–81

*L*OVE'S SECRET

Never seek to tell thy love,
  Love that never told can be;
For the gentle wind doth move
  Silently, invisibly.

I told my love, I told my love,
  I told her all my heart,
Trembling, cold, in ghastly fears,
  Ah! she did depart!

Soon after she was gone from me,
  A traveller came by,
Silently, invisibly:
  He took her with a sigh.

WILLIAM BLAKE 1757–1827

A NEW-FOUND LOVE

As I rose and dressed, I thought over what had happened, and wondered if it were a dream. I could not be certain of the reality till I had seen Mr Rochester again, and heard him renew his words of love and promise.

While arranging my hair, I looked at my face in the glass, and felt it was no longer plain: there was hope in its aspects and life in its colour; and my eyes seemed as if they had beheld the fount of fruition, and borrowed beams from the lustrous ripple. I had often been unwilling to look at my master, because I feared he could not be pleased at my look: but I was sure I might lift my face to his now, and not cool his affection by its expression. I took a plain but clean and light summer dress from my drawer and put it on: it seemed no attire had ever so well become me, because none had I ever worn in so blissful a mood.

I was not surprised, when I ran down into the hall, to see that a brillant June morning had succeeded to the tempest of the night; and to feel, through the open glass door, the breathing of a fresh and fragrant breeze. Nature must be gladsome when I was so happy. I met Adèle leaving the schoolroom.

'Where are you going? It is time for lessons.'

'Mr Rochester has sent me away to the nursery.'

'Where is he?'

'In there,' pointing to the apartment she had left; and I went in, and there he stood.

'Come and bid me good-morning,' said he. I gladly advanced; and it was not merely a cold word now, or even a shake of the hand that I received, but an embrace and a kiss. It seemed natural: it seemed genial to be so well loved, so caressed by him.

'Jane, you look blooming, and smiling, and pretty,' said he: 'truly pretty this morning. Is this my pale little elf? Is this my mustard-seed? This little sunny-faced girl with the dimpled cheek and rosy lips; the satin-smooth hazel hair, and the radiant hazel eyes?' (I had green eyes, reader; but you must excuse the mistake; for him they were new-dyed, I suppose.)

'It is Jane Eyre, sir.'

Jane Eyre, CHARLOTTE BRONTË 1816 55

BOLDWOOD'S PROPOSAL

Boldwood came close and bade her good morning with such constraint that she could not but think he had stepped across to the washing for its own sake, hoping not to find her there; more, she fancied his brow severe and his eye slighting. Bathsheba immediately contrived to withdraw, and glided along by the river till she was a stone's throw off. She heard footsteps brushing the grass, and had a consciousness that love was encircling her like a perfume. Instead of turning or waiting, Bathsheba went further among the high sedges, but Boldwood seemed determined, and pressed on till they were completely past the bend of the river. Here, without being seen, they could hear the splashing and shouts of the washers above.

'Miss Everdene!' said the farmer.

She trembled, turned, and said 'Good morning.' His tone was so utterly removed from all she had expected as a beginning. It was lowness and quiet accentuated: an emphasis of deep meanings, their form, at the same time, being scarcely expressed. Silence has sometimes a remarkable power of showing itself as the disembodied soul of feeling wandering without its carcase, and it is then more impressive than speech. In the same way, to say a little is often to tell more than to say a great deal. Boldwood told everything in that word.

As the consciousness expands on learning that what was fancied to be the rumble of wheels is the reverberation of thunder, so did Bathsheba's at her intuitive conviction.

'I feel – almost too much – to think,' he said, with a solemn simplicity. 'I have come to speak to you without preface. My life is not my own since I have beheld you clearly, Miss Everdene – I come to make you an offer of marriage.'

Bathsheba tried to preserve an absolutely neutral counten⁄ance, and all the motion she made was that of closing lips which had previously been a little parted.

'I am now forty-one years old,' he went on. 'I may have been called a confirmed bachelor, and I was a confirmed bachelor. I had never any views of myself as a husband in my earlier days, nor have I made any calculation on the subject since I have been older. But we all change, and my change, in this matter, came with seeing you. I have felt lately, more and more, that my present way of living is bad in every respect. Beyond all things, I want you as my wife.'

'I feel, Mr Boldwood, that though I respect you much, I do not feel – what would justify me to – in accepting your offer,' she stammered.

This giving back of dignity for dignity seemed to open the sluices of feeling that Boldwood had as yet kept closed.

'My life is a burden without you,' he exclaimed, in a low voice. 'I want you – I want you to let me say I love you again and again!'

Far from the Madding Crowd, THOMAS HARDY 1840–1928

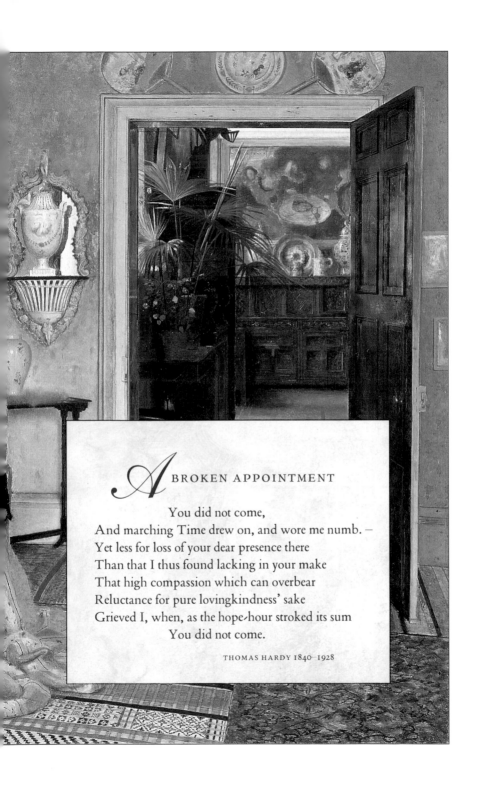

A BROKEN APPOINTMENT

You did not come,
And marching Time drew on, and wore me numb. –
Yet less for loss of your dear presence there
Than that I thus found lacking in your make
That high compassion which can overbear
Reluctance for pure lovingkindness' sake
Grieved I, when, as the hope-hour stroked its sum
You did not come.

THOMAS HARDY 1840–1928

MUTUAL PLEASURE

I cannot say that Paulina designedly led him to talk of books, or formally proposed to herself for a moment the task of winning him to reflection, or planned the improvement of his mind, or so much as fancied his mind could in any one respect be improved. She thought him very perfect. Each liked the way in which the other talked; the voice, the diction, the expression pleased; each keenly relished the flavour of the other's wit; they met each other's meaning with strange quickness, their thoughts often matched like carefully-chosen pearls. Graham had wealth of mirth by nature; Paulina possessed no such inherent flow of animal spirits – unstimulated, she inclined to be thoughtful and pensive – but now she seemed merry as a lark; in her lover's genial presence, she glanced like some soft glad light. How beautiful she grew in her happiness, I can hardly express, but I wondered to see her. As to that gentle ice of hers – that reserve on which she had depended; where was it now? Ah! Graham would not long bear it; he brought with him a generous influence that soon thawed the timid, self-imposed restriction.

Villette, CHARLOTTE BRONTË 1816-55

I WAIT FOR A SIGN

In the deep violet air,
   Not a leaf is stirred;
   There is no sound heard,
But afar, the rare
   Trilled voice of a bird.

Is the wood's dim heart,
   And the fragrant pine,
   Incense, and a shrine
Of her coming? Apart,
   I wait for a sign.

What the sudden hush said,
   She will hear, and forsake,
   Swift, for my sake,
Her green, grassy bed:
   She will hear and awake!

She will hearken and glide,
   From her place of deep rest,
   Dove-eyed, with the breast
Of a dove, to my side;
   The pines bow their crest.

ERNEST DOWSON 1867–1900

HE GOOD-MORROW

I wonder by my troth, what thou, and I
Did, till we lov'd? were we not wean'd till then?
But suck'd on country pleasures, childishly?
Or snorted we i'the seven sleepers den?
'Twas so; But this, all pleasures fancies be.
If ever any beauty I did see,
Which I desir'd, and got, 'twas but a dream of thee.

And now good morrow to our waking souls,
Which watch not one another out of fear;
For love, all love of other sights controls,
And makes one little room, an every where.
Let sea-discoverers to new worlds have gone,
Let Maps to others, worlds on worlds have shown,
Let us possess our world, each hath one, and is one.

My face in thine eye, thine in mine appears,
And true plain hearts do in the faces rest,
Where can we find two better hemispheres
Without sharp North, without declining West?
What ever dies, was not mixt equally;
If our two loves be one, or, thou and I
Love so alike, that none do slacken, none can die

JOHN DONNE 1572 1631

WOMAN MUCH MISSED

Woman much missed, how you call to me, call to me,
Saying that now you are not as you were
When you had changed from the one who was all to me,
But as at first, when our day was fair.

Can it be you that I hear? Let me view you, then,
Standing as when I drew near to the town
Where you would wait for me: yes, as I knew you then,
Even to the original air-blue gown!

Or is it only the breeze, in its listlessness
Travelling across the wet mead to me here,
You being ever dissolved to wan wistlessness,
Heard no more again far or near?

Thus I; faltering forward,
Leaves around me falling,
Wind oozing thin through the thorn from norward,
And the woman calling.

THOMAS HARDY 1840-1928

TO HELEN

Helen, thy beauty is to me
    Like those Nicean barks of yore,
That gently, o'er a perfumed sea,
    The weary, wayworn wanderer bore
    To his own native shore.

On desperate seas long wont to roam,
    Thy hyacinth hair, thy classic face,
Thy Naiad airs have brought me home
    To the glory that was Greece,
    To the grandeur that was Rome.

Lo! in yon brilliant window niche,
    How statue-like I see thee stand,
    The agate lamp within thy hand!
Ah, Psyche, from the regions which
    Are Holy Land!

EDGAR ALLAN POE 1809–49

[52]

THE RAGGED WOOD

O hurry where by water among the trees
The delicate-stepping stag and his lady sigh,
When they have but looked upon their images —
Would none had ever loved but you and I!

Or have you heard that sliding silver-shoed
Pale silver-proud queen-woman of the sky,
When the sun looked out of his golden hood? —
O that none ever loved but you and I!

O hurry to the ragged wood, for there
I will drive all those lovers out and cry —
O my share of the world, O yellow hair!
No one has ever loved but you and I!

W. B. YEATS 1865–1939

O WHAT CAN AIL THEE

O what can ail thee, knight‑at‑arms,
  Alone and palely loitering?
The sedge has wither'd from the lake,
  And no birds sing.

I see a lily on thy brow
  With anguish moist and fever dew,
And on thy cheeks a fading rose
  Fast withereth too.

I met a lady in the meads,
    Full beautiful — a faery's child,
Her hair was long, her foot was light,
    And her eyes were wild.

I set her on my pacing steed,
    And nothing else saw all day long,
For sidelong would she bend, and sing
    A faery's song.

She took me to her elfin grot,
    And there she wept and sigh'd full sore,
And there I shut her wild wild eyes
    With kisses four.

And there she lulled me asleep,
    And there I dream'd — ah! woe betide!
The latest dream I ever dream'd
    On the cold hill's side.

I saw pale kings and princes too,
    Pale warriors, death-pale were they all;
They cried — 'La Belle Dame sans Merci
    Hath thee in thrall!'

I saw their starved lips in the gloam,
    With horrid warning gaped wide,
And I awoke and found me here,
    On the cold hill's side.

And this is why I sojourn here,
    Alone and palely loitering,
Though the sedge is wither'd from the lake,
    And no birds sing.

JOHN KEATS 1795–1821

$\mathcal{V}$ENETIAN ROMANCE

Nothing could exceed Emily's admiration on her first view of Venice, with its islets, palaces, and towers rising out of the sea, whose clear surface reflected the tremulous picture in all its colours. The barge stopped before the portico of a large house, from whence a servant of Montoni crossed the terrace, and immediately the party disembarked. From the portico they passed a noble hall to a staircase of marble, which led to a saloon fitted up in a style of magnificence that surprised Emily. The walls and ceilings were adorned with historical and allegorical paintings in fresco; silver tripods depending from chains of the same metal illuminated the apartment, the floor of which was covered with Indian mats painted in a variety of colours and devices; the couches and drapery of the lattices were of pale green silk, embroidered and fringed with green and gold. Balcony lattices opened upon the Grand Canal, whence rose a confusion of voices and of musical instruments, and the breeze that gave freshness to the apartment. ... Emily ... withdrew to a lattice, to amuse herself with the scene without, so new and so enchanting.

The first object that attracted her attention was a group of minstrels . . . They sung in parts, their voices accompanied by a few soft instruments. At a little distance from the portico they stopped, and Emily distinguished the verses of Ariosto, They sung of the wars of Charlemagne, and then of the woes of Orlando: afterwards the measure changed, and the melancholy sweetness of Petrarch succeeded. The magic of his grief was assisted by all that Italian expression, heightened by the enchantments of Venetian moonlight, could give.

Emily, as she listened, caught the pensive enthusiasm; her tears flowed silently, while her fancy bore her away to France and to Valancourt. Each succeeding sonnet, more full of charming sadness than the last, seemed to bind the spell of melancholy: with extreme regret she saw the musicians move on.

The last strain of distant music now died in air, for the gondola was far upon the waves, and the party determined to have music of their own. The Count Morano, who sat next to Emily and who had been observing her for some time in silence, snatched up a lute, and struck the chords with the finger of harmony herself, while his voice, a fine tenor, accompanied them in a rondeau full of tender sadness.

The Mysteries of Udolpho, ANN RADCLIFFE 1764–1823

To LUCASTA, GOING TO THE WARS

Tell me not, Sweet, I am unkind
    That from the nunnery
Of thy chaste breasts, and quiet mind,
    To war and arms I fly.

True, a new mistress now I chase,
    The first foe in the field;
And with a stronger faith embrace
    A sword, a horse, a shield.

Yet this inconstancy is such
    As you too shall adore;
I could not love there, Dear, so much,
    Loved I not honour more.

RICHARD LOVELACE 1618-58

To Electra

I dare not ask a kisse;
    I dare not beg a smile;
Lest having that, or this,
    I might grow proud the while.

No, no, the utmost share
    Of my desire, shall be
Onely to kisse that Aire,
    That lately kissed thee.

ROBERT HERRICK 1591–1674

THE SILENT LOVER

Passions are liken'd best to floods and streams:
  The shallow murmur, but the deep are dumb;
So, when affection yields discourse, it seems
  The bottom is but shallow whence they come.
They that are rich in words, in words discover
That they are poor in that which makes a lover.

SIR WALTER RALEGH 1552–1618

$\mathscr{V}$ALENTINE

Upon this day one secret of my heart,
   Till now concealed, shall truly be confessed.
If there's a youth whose love I would command,
To whom resign my maiden heart and hand:
   You are that youth to whose oft preferred vow,
Of Love and Constancy I answer now;
   If still unchanged for me alone you live,
Let your reply that fond assurance give.

Valentine, NINETEETH CENTURY

$\mathcal{M}$Y TRUE LOVE HATH MY HEART

My true love hath my heart, and I have his,
By just exchange one for another given.
I hold his dear, and mine he cannot miss:
There never was a better bargain driven,
My true love hath my heart and I have his.

His heart in me, keeps him and me in one,
My heart in him, his thoughts and senses guides:
He loves my heart, for once it was his own:
I cherish his, because in me it bides.
My true love hath my heart and I have his.

SIR PHILIP SIDNEY 1554–86

'To fall in with each other on such an errand as this,' thought Emma; 'to meet in a charitable scheme; this will bring a great increase of love on each side. I should not wonder if it were to bring on the declaration. It must, if I were not here. I wish I were anywhere else.'

Anxious to separate herself from them as far as she could, she soon afterwards took possession of a narrow footpath, a little raised on one side of the lane, leaving them together in the main road. But she had not been there two minutes when she found that Harriet's habits of dependence and imitation were bringing her up too, and that, in short, they would both be soon after her. This would not do; she immediately stopped, under pretence of having some alteration to make in the lacing of her half-boot, and stooping down in complete occupation of the footpath, begged them to have the goodness to walk on, and she would follow in half a minute. They did as they were desired; and by the time she judged it reasonable to have done with her boot, Mr Elton was speaking with animation. Harriet listening with a very pleased attention; and Emma was beginning to think how she might draw back a little more, when they both looked around, and she was obliged to join them.

Mr Elton was still talking, still engaged in some interesting detail; and Emma experienced some disappointment when she found that he was only giving his fair companion an account of the yesterday's party at his friend Cole's, and that she was come in herself for the Stilton cheese, the north Wiltshire, the butter, the cellery, the beet-root and all the dessert.

'This would soon have led to something better of course,' was her consoling reflection; 'any thing interests between those who love; and any thing will serve as introduction to what is near the heart. If I could but have kept longer away!'

They now walked on together quietly, till within view of the vicarage pales, when a sudden resolution, of at least getting Harriet into the house, made her again find something very much amiss about her boot, and fall behind to arrange it once more. She then broke the lace off short, and dexterously throwing it into a ditch, was presently obliged to entreat them to stop, and acknowledge her inability to put herself to rights so as to be able to walk home in tolerable comfort.

'Part of my lace is gone,' said she, 'and I do not know how I am to contrive. I really am a most troublesome companion to you both, but I hope I am not often so ill-equipped. Mr Elton, I must beg leave to stop at your house, and ask your housekeeper for a bit of ribband or string, or any thing just to keep my boot on.'

Mr Elton looked all happiness at this proposition; and nothing could exceed his alertness and attention in conducting them into his house and endeavouring to make every thing appear to advantage. The room they were taken into was the one he chiefly occupied, and looking forwards; behind it was another with which it immediately communicated; the door between them was open, and Emma passed into it with the housekeeper to receive her assistance in the most comfortable manner. She was obliged to leave the door ajar as she found it; but she fully intended that Mr Elton should close it. It was not closed however, it still remained ajar; but by engaging the housekeeper in incessant conversation, she hoped to make it practicable for him to chuse his own subject in the adjoining room. For ten minutes she could hear nothing but herself. It could be protracted no longer. She was then obliged to be finished and make her appearance.

The lovers were standing together at one of the windows. It had a most favourable aspect; and, for half a minute, Emma felt the glory of having schemed successfully. But it would not do; he had not come to the point. He had been most agreeable, most delightful; he had told Harriet that he had seen them go by, and had purposely followed them; other little gallantries and allusions had been dropt, but nothing serious.

'Cautious, very cautious,' thought Emma; 'he advances inch by inch, and will hazard nothing till he believes himself secure.'

Still, however, though every thing had not been accomplished by her ingenious device, she could not but flatter herself that it had been the occasion of much present enjoyment to both, and must be leading them forward to the great event.

Emma, JANE AUSTEN 1775-1817

ONE DAY I WROTE HER NAME UPON THE STRAND

One day I wrote her name upon the strand,
But came the waves and washèd it away:
Again I wrote it with a second hand,
But came the tide, and made my pains his prey.
Vain man, said she, that dost in vain assay,
A mortal thing so to immortalise,
But I myself shall like to this decay,
And eke my name be wipèd out likewise.
Not so (quod I), let baser things devise
To die in dust, but you shall live by fame:
My verse your virtues rare shall eternise,
And in the heavens write your glorious name.
    Where whenas death shall all the world subdue,
    Our love shall live, and later life renew.

EDMUND SPENSER 1552–99

May Guardian Angels Still Protect Thee

May peace be ever round thy dwelling,
    And all that's good on thee attend;
And may each morn with pleasure smiling,
    Hail thee still, my lovely friend.

And whether in the bustling town,
    Or in the country's calm retreat,
May fortune never on thee frown,
    Nor envy grudge thy better fate.

May slander's darts fall far behind thee,
    Or pointed back against thy foe,

Still may the honest heart befriend thee,
    And guard you safe where'er you go.

Oh! may you never drop a tear,
    Except for sorrows not your own;
Or for the friend you loved so dear,
    In tribute to the worth that's gone.

Far be the man that would attempt
    To lead you from fair virtues way,
Ye powers above! Do ye prevent
    The tongue that flatters to betray.

And ever free from rude alarms,
    In happiness long may you live;
Blest with a faithful lover's arms,
    With all that worldly wealth can give.

May guardian angels still protect thee,
    Whereso'er you chance to roam;
And should the base world ever vex you,
    Oh! Make *my bosom* still *your home.*

Valentine, NINETEENTH CENTURY

[73]

To a Sempstress

Oh what bosom but must yield,
 When, like Pallas, you advance,
With a thimble for your shield,
 And a needle for your lance?

Fairest of the stitching train,
 Ease my passion by your art;
And, in pity to my pain,
 Mend the hole that's in my heart.

ANON. EIGHTEENTH CENTURY

 # OR YOU ALONE

Dearest Anne

I can listen no longer in silence. I must speak to you by such means as are within my reach. You pierce my soul. I am half agony, half hope. Tell me not that I am too late, that such precious feelings are gone for ever. I offer myself to you again with a heart even more your own, than when you almost broke it eight years and a half ago. Dare not say that man forgets sooner than woman, that his love has an earlier death. I have loved none but you. Unjust I may have been, weak and resentful I have been, but never inconstant. You alone have brought me to Bath. For you alone I think and plan. – Have you not seen this? Can you fail to have understood my wishes? – I had not waited even these ten days, could I have read your feelings, as I think you must have penetrated mine. I can hardly write. I am every instant hearing something which overpowers me. You sink your voice, but I can distinguish the tones of that voice, when they would be lost on others. – Too good, too excellent creature! You do us justice indeed. You do believe that there is true attachment and constancy among men. Believe it to be most fervent, most undeviating in – Wentworth.

Persuasion, JANE AUSTEN 1775 1817

I LOVE YOU EVER AND EVER

Sweetest Fanny,

You fear, sometimes, I do not love you so much as you wish? My dear Girl I love you ever and ever and without reserve. The more I have known you the more have I lov'd. In every way — even my jealousies have been agonies of Love, in the hottest fit I ever had I would have died for you. I have vex'd you too much. But for Love! Can I help it? You are always new. The last of your kisses was ever the sweetest; the last smile the brightest; the last movement the gracefullest. When you pass'd my window home yesterday, I was fill'd with as much admiration as if I had then seen you for the first time. You uttered a half complaint once that I only lov'd your Beauty. Have I nothing else then to love in you but that? Do not I see a heart naturally furnish'd with wings imprison itself with me? No ill prospect has been able to turn your thoughts a moment from me. This perhaps should be as much a subject of sorrow as joy — but I will not talk of that. Even if you did not love me I could not help an entire devotion to you: how much more deeply then must I feel for you knowing you love me. My Mind has been the most discontented and restless one that ever was put into a body too small for it. I never felt my Mind repose upon anything with complete and undistracted enjoyment — upon no person but you. When you are in the room my thoughts never fly out of window; you always concentrate my whole senses. The anxiety shown about our Loves in your last note is an immense

pleasure to me: however you must not suffer such speculations
to molest you any more: nor will I any more believe you can
have the least pique against me. Brown is gone out – but here is
Mrs Wylie – when she is gone I shall be awake for you. –
Remembrances to your Mother.

Your affectionate

J. Keats

JOHN KEATS 1795–1821

[79]

O LOVE, WHAT HOURS WERE THINE AND MINE

O love, what hours were thine and mine,
In lands of palm and southern pine;
   In lands of palm, of orange-blossom,
Of olive, aloe, and maize and vine.

Nor knew we well what pleased us most,
Not the clipt palm of which they boast;
   But distant colour, happy hamlet,
A moulder'd citadel on the coast,

Or tower, or high hill-convent, seen
A light amid its olives green;
   Or olive-hoary cape in ocean;
Or rosy blossom in hot ravine.

What more? we took our last adieu,
And up the snowy Splugen drew,
    But ere we reach'd the highest summit
I pluck'd a daisy, I gave it you.

It told of England then to me,
And now it tells of Italy.
    O love, we two shall go no longer
To lands of summer across the sea;

So dear a life your arms enfold
Whose crying is a cry for gold:
    Yet here to-night in this dark city,
When ill and weary, alone and cold,

I found, tho' crush'd to hard and dry,
This nursling of another sky
    Still in the little book you lent me,
And where you tenderly laid it by:

And I forgot the clouded Forth,
The gloom that saddens Heaven and Earth
    The bitter east, the misty summer
And gray metropolis of the North.

Perchance, to lull the throbs of pain,
Perchance, to charm a vacant brain,
    Perchance, to dream you still beside me,
My fancy fled to the South again.

ALFRED, LORD TENNYSON 1809–92

[81]

D ID NOT

'Twas a new feeling – something more
Than we had dared to own before,
 Which then we hid not;
We saw it in each other's eye,
And wished, in every half-breathed sigh,
 To speak, but did not.

She felt my lips' impassioned touch –
'Twas the first time I dared so much,
 And yet she chid not;
But whispered o'er my burning brow,
'Oh, do you doubt I love you now?'
 Sweet soul! I did not.

Warmly I felt her bosom thrill,
I pressed it closer, closer still,
 Though gently bid not;
Till – oh! the world hath seldom heard
Of lovers, who so nearly erred,
 And yet, who did not.

THOMAS MOORE 1779–1852

$\mathscr{Y}$OU ARE A PRISONER, MISS

He looked hard into her eyes when she raised them for a moment; Bathsheba looked down again, for his gaze was too strong to be received point-blank with her own. But she had obliquely noticed that he was young and slim, and that he wore three chevrons upon his sleeve.

Bathsheba pulled again.

'You are a prisoner, miss; it is no use blinking the matter,' said the soldier drily.

She withdrew her own hand, but, whether by accident or design, he touched it. Bathsheba was vexed; she hardly knew why.

She looked at him again.

'Thank you for the sight of such a beautiful face!' said the young sergeant, without ceremony.

She coloured with embarrassment. ''Twas unwillingly shown,' she replied stiffly, and with as much dignity – which was very little – as she could infuse into a position of captivity.

'I like you the better for that incivility, miss,' he said.

Bathsheba was revolving in her mind whether by a bold and desperate rush she could free herself at the risk of leaving her skirt bodily behind her. The thought was too dreadful. The dress – which she had put on to appear stately at the supper – was the head and front of her wardrobe; not another in her stock became her so well. What woman in Bathsheba's position, not naturally timid, and within call of her retainers, would have bought escape from a dashing soldier at so dear a price?

'All in good time; it will soon be done, I perceive,' said her cool friend.

'This trifling provokes, and – and – '

'Not too cruel!'

'– Insults me!'

'It is done in order that I may have pleasure of apologizing to so charming a woman, which I straightway do most humbly, madam,' he said, bowing low.

Bathsheba really knew not what to say.

'I've seen a good many women in my time,' continued the young man in a murmur, and more thoughtfully than hitherto, critically regarding her bent head at the same time; 'but I've never seen a woman so beautiful as you. Take it or leave it – be offended or like it – I don't care.'

'Who are you, then, who can so well afford to despise opinion?'

'No stranger. Sergeant Troy. I am staying in this place. – There! it is undone at last, you see. Your light fingers were more eager than mine. I wish it had been the knot of knots, which there's no untying!'

Far from the Madding Crowd, THOMAS HARDY 1840–1928

AFETY

Dear! of all happy in the hour, most blest
   He who has found our hid security,
Assured in the dark tides of the world that rest,
   And heard our word, 'Who is so safe as we?'
We have found safety with all things undying,
   The winds, and morning, tears of men and mirth,
The deep night, and birds singing, and clouds flying,
   And sleep, and freedom, and the autumnal earth.

RUPERT BROOKE 1887–1915

MARRIAGE BY LICENCE

The marriage being by licence there were only a dozen or so of people in the church. In the ecstatic solemnity with which she swore her faith to him the ordinary sensibilities of sex seemed a flippancy. At a pause in the service, while they were kneeling together, she unconsciously inclined herself towards him, so that her shoulder touched his arm; she had been frightened by a passing thought, and the movement had been automatic, to assure herself that he was really there, and to fortify her belief that his fidelity would be proof against all things.

Clare knew that she loved him – every curve of her form showed that – but he did not know at that time the full depth of her devotion, its single-mindedness, its meekness; what long-suffering it guaranteed, what honesty, what endurance, what good faith.

As they came out of church the ringers swung the bells off their rests, and a modest peal of three notes broke forth – that limited amount of expression having been deemed sufficient by the church builders for the joys of such a small parish. Passing by the tower with her husband on the path to the gate she could feel the vibrant air humming round them from the louvred belfry in a circle of sound, and it matched the highly-charged mental atmosphere in which she was living.

Tess of the d'Urbervilles, THOMAS HARDY 1840–1928

THE ROSE

The rose will cease to blow,
    The eagle turn a dove,
The stream will cease to flow,
    Ere I will cease to love.

The sun will cease to shine,
    The world will cease to move,
The stars their light resign,
    Ere I will cease to love.

ANON. NINETEENTH CENTURY

$\mathcal{T}$HE KISS

'I saw you take his kiss!' ''Tis true.'
'O, modesty!' ''Twas strictly kept;
He thought me asleep; at least I knew
He thought I thought he thought I slept.'

COVENTRY PATMORE 1832–96

MEDIOCRITY IN LOVE REJECTED

Give me more love, or more disdain;
  The torrid or the frozen zone
Bring equal ease unto my pain;
  The temperate affords me none:
Either extreme, of love or hate,
Is sweeter than a calm estate.

THOMAS CAREW 1595–1639

ACKNOWLEDGEMENTS

The publishers would like to thank the following for permission to reproduce. Bury Street Gallery pp. 26, 38, 42–3, 54–5, 76; Cecil Higgins Art Gallery, The Trustees, Bedford p. 13; Christie's pp. 6, 15, 19, 24, 50, 56, 64–5, 71, 72, 87; Christopher Wood Gallery p. 80; Fine Art Photographic Library Ltd. pp. 22–3, 30–1, 32, 37, 41, 44, 47, 61, 62, 67, 79, 89, 90, 91; Hugh Lane Municipal Gallery of Modern Art, Dublin p. 53; Maas Gallery pp. 18, 34; Manchester City Art Galleries frontispiece, pp. 21, 92–3; Mary Evans Picture Library p. 4; McCormick Collection p. 36; Nottingham Castle Museum and Art Gallery pp. 74–5; Private Collection p. 69; Sotheby's p. 8; The Bridgeman Art Library with acknowledgements to: Bradford Art Galleries and Museums pp. 82–3; City of York Art Gallery p. 16, Galerie George, London p. 58, Guildhall Art Gallery, London pp. 10–11, 28, Private Collection p. 66, Towneley Hall Art Gallery and Museums, Burnley p. 49; Walker Art Gallery, Liverpool p. 84 and to A. P. Watt Ltd, on behalf of the Literary Executors of the Estate of H. G. Wells p. 29 (abridged).

LIST OF PAINTINGS

Cover and frontispiece: *Girl Reading*, Pergini; p. 4 *C.19 Valentine's Card*; p. 6 *Pastoral*, Lord Leighton; p. 8 *Woman Seated*, Marcus Stone; pp. 10–11 *Pleading*, Alma-Tadema; p. 13 *Paolo and Francesca*, Rossetti; p. 15 *October*, Tissot; p. 16 *Mated*, Frank Stone; p. 18 *The Offering*, Sir F. Dicksee; p. 19 *Fair Rosamund*, J. Waterhouse; p. 21 *On the Threshold*, E. Leighton; pp. 22–3 *The Prince's Choice*, T. R. Lamont; p. 24 *Elizabeth Siddal*, Rossetti; p. 26 *Woman in White*, Gaston Latouche; p. 28 *The Garden of Eden*, H. G. Riviere; pp. 30–1 *A Romantic Picnic*, A. Serrure; p. 32 *Hearts are Trumps*, G. G. Kilburne; p. 34 *The Flower Seller*, A. E. Mulready; p. 36 *Portrait of a Wife*, F. Goodall; p. 37 *Roses in a Basket*, Looschen; p. 38 *Woman Seated*, Carlo Holsoe; p. 41 *The Lovers' Tryst*, Richard Redgrave; pp. 42–3 *Summer*, J. Atkinson Grimshaw; p. 44 *Derby Day*, W. P. Frith; p. 47 *At the Fountain*, L. C. Nightingale; p. 49 *I Will*, Francois Brunery; p. 50 *The Telephone Call*, Gaston Latouche; p. 53 *Azaleas*, Albert Moore; pp. 54–5 *Gardens at Versailles*, Gaston Latouche; p. 56 *Sir Galahad*, G. F. Watts; p. 58 *The Lover's Gift*, Nicaise de Keyser; p. 61 *The Riven Shield*, P. R. Morris; p. 62 *Divinely Fair*, H. T. Schafer; pp. 64–5 *On the Bank*, P. Ilstead; p. 66 *The Year's at the Spring*, Alma-Tadema; p. 67 *Love at the Stile*, Marcus Stone; p. 69 *Showing a Preference*, J. C. Horsley; p. 71 *Near Leoni*, Andersen-Lundby; p. 72 *The Proposal*, H. Singleton; pp. 74–5 *In Love*, Marcus Stone; p. 76 *Woman Reading a Letter*, Carl Holsoe; p. 79 *Roses*, E. H. Stannard; p. 80 *Where Next?* E. F. Brewtnall; pp. 82–3 *Gather Ye Rosebuds While Ye May*, T. B. Wirgman; p. 84 *Black Brunswicker*, J. E. Millais; p. 87 *Resting on the Terrace*, Luigi Rossi; p. 89 *Betrothed*, W. Savage Cooper; p. 90 *Carnations*, Leo Louppe; p. 91 *The Stolen Kiss*, Marcus Stone; pp. 92–3 *A Passing Cloud*, Marcus Stone.

Compiled and designed for Victoria's Secret in Great Britain by
George Weidenfeld & Nicolson Limited
91 Clapham High Street
LONDON SW4 7TA

Printed and bound in Italy